x

**SCHOLASTIC**

Book End, Range Road, Witney, Oxfordshire, OX29 OYD
www.scholastic.co.uk
© 2013, Scholastic Ltd

2 3 4 5 6 7 8 9   4 5 6 7 8 9 0 1 2

British Library Cataloguing-in-Publication Data
A catalogue record for this book is available from the
British Library.

ISBN 978-1407-12792-7
Printed by Bell & Bain Ltd, Glasgow

Text © Paul Hollin 2013

**Commissioning Editor**
Paul Naish

**Development Editor**
Pollyanna Poulter

**Editor**
Kate Pedlar

**Proofreader**
Kate Manson

**Series Designer**
Shelley Best

**Illustrator**
Paul Hutchinson

*Acknowledgements*
The publishers gratefully acknowledge permission
to reproduce the following copyright material:

**Cover:** planets © jut13/iStockphoto.com
**Pages 14 and 15:** coins © The Royal Mint
**Page 29:** large tile pattern © Ryan KC Wong/
iStockphoto.com, small tile pattern © Luis Alvarez/
iStockphoto.com

*About the author*
Paul Hollin worked for many years in teaching,
starting as a maths tutor for the Home Tutors
Teachers' Cooperative in London. After stints doing
photography in youth clubs and teaching English in
Spain and London, he eventually became a primary
teacher working mainly with junior-aged children.
He left the classroom to work for Sherston
Software, where he designed a wide range
of educational software and now works in
educational publishing, writing and providing
consultancy in a freelance capacity.

# Contents

## About the series

*Real-Life Maths* is a series of three books designed to supplement your maths curriculum. Each book provides a wide range of extended scenarios that develop many maths skills in engaging and meaningful contexts, often involving significant child interaction. The three books are categorised by age range, although teachers will find materials suitable for their classes across the series as the activities are relatively age neutral. The planning grids for the books are available on each respective CD-ROM.

## The importance of real-life maths

Anyone who keeps their eye on the educational news will know that maths is a hot topic: standards aren't good enough; adults can't add up; other countries do it better, and so on. Why is it thus? It is interesting to compare maths with literacy; between the two they form the bedrock of primary education. There are many technical aspects to developing a child's capabilities in literacy – these are sometimes taught discretely and sometimes integrated. Either way, every primary school in the land uses real sources of language, such as books, newspapers and drama, to aid pupils' literacy development; not to mention the myriad of approaches for writing in context – letters, stories, poems, and more.

Now look at maths. The majority of maths lessons involve the discrete teaching of specific skills, be it the four operations, factors, or shape. The nature of maths dictates this to some extent, but it can leave those being taught it fundamentally baffled – why are they learning it? Now, *we* know why – being numerate is essential in adult life – but, and here's the crux of the matter, in adult life nearly all of us use our numeracy skills in meaningful situations. These books do not suggest that you should fundamentally alter your maths curriculum, but by simply adding a regular dose of real-life maths, as well as engaging and motivating your pupils, they will see the point of it all. Real-life maths activities are not just about getting the right answers. Mistakes can be useful, allowing children to see that the consequence of an error is not simply a cross and a correction: an error might result in an incorrect design, getting lost, or even losing money.

## About the activities

There are ten real-life scenarios per book, each one providing a multi-session, structured scenario complete with teacher guidance and resources on paper and the accompanying CD-ROM. Typically, a scenario will take between two and four lessons to complete. Every scenario has a practical focus, where the maths is an integral part of a greater task – just like life!

The scenarios are arranged in roughly increasing levels of difficulty, and between them they cover a wide range of maths skills, often with several skills being involved in any one activity. In addition, because of their focus on the real world, the scenarios have cross-curricular links, and most primary subjects are covered.

The activities are all fairly challenging. They require extended thinking and clear organisation of work, as well as making demands on children's mathematical thinking. Some can be done by individuals, though many would benefit from paired or group work, and some involve whole-class participation in highly 'immersive' situations.

## Scenario content

Each scenario covers four pages in the book, and typically consists of:

**1. Teacher notes**

Mathematics coverage; guidance on organising and running lessons; tips for differentiation; review and further ideas.

**2. Scenario guidelines**

Introducing the scenario; guidelines and 'rules'; additional information; worked examples where appropriate.

**3. Resources and information**

Typically this page has all of the mathematical and factual information needed to run the scenario.

**4. Recording sheet**

Typically this page provides a template for children to use to lay out their work, though sometimes additional paper is required.

## CD-ROM content

For every activity there is extensive supporting material on the CD-ROM, including an introductory video and slideshow, which set the scene. In addition, all photocopiables are available on the CD-ROM for easy printing. Most activities have further support sheets which can be printed, and some have additional resources, such as simple chart and graphing tools.

## Planning and running real-life maths sessions

Good learning and good lessons come at a price – real-life maths scenarios require preparation. Teachers will need to familiarise themselves with the scenario in advance, as well as prepare resources.

How you weave the lessons into your curriculum will depend on your general approach to teaching. Do you want to challenge children by presenting activities that are in their 'zone of development', or do you prefer to consolidate well-honed skills?

Typically, the first lesson is about introducing the scenario to the class. There is an introduction for each activity on the CD-ROM which, while not essential, does provide a clear overview of the context and situation. In addition, introducing or recapping the key maths skills involved is encouraged. Children may also need to do some planning in advance of the second lesson.

The second lesson is where the scenario really gets underway. Ideally, having more than an hour available would be useful if things are progressing well. However long you spend, a plenary review is encouraged afterwards, where broader issues of the purpose of the maths as well as the maths skills involved can be discussed.

Subsequent lessons, either repetitions with variation or extensions, are also possible at your discretion – and if you are inspired there are ideas for further work in the teacher notes for each scenario, as well as guidance at the back of the book.

**Remember**, the activities in all three books are relatively age neutral in tone, and can be used effectively to challenge or support children in other age groups, and all three books' planning grids are on the CD-ROM.

| Ages 7–9 | Pages 8–11 | Pages 12–15 | Pages 16–19 | Pages 20–23 | Pages 24–27 |
|---|---|---|---|---|---|
| **Scenario** | 1. Pizza please! | 2. Tumbletown | 3. A brief history of inventions | 4. School sports day | 5. Mr Wolf's DIY shop |
| **Focus** | Create pizzas to order by reading charts and calculating costs. | Tourists pay rickshaw drivers fares to visit a range of attractions. | Organise a range of inventions in order. | Children take part in a virtual sports day, with random results generated each time. | Design and cost different houses for the three little pigs. |
| **Difficulty rating (3 max.)** | ★ | ★ | ★ | ★★ | ★★ |
| **Maths covered** | ● Reading charts<br>● Calculating costs<br>● Basic fractions<br>● Adding to 20 and beyond | ● Adding and subtracting to 20, 50 or 100<br>● Money<br>● Time (optional) | ● Ordering 1000–2000<br>● Using knowledge of number bonds to 20 to solve problems with larger numbers (extension) | ● Using simple formulae<br>● Multiply and divide by 2<br>● Subtracting TU from 50<br>● Adding to over 100<br>● Checking with a calculator | ● Calculating costs up to and over 100, involving money<br>● Basic scale and measuring<br>● Simple nets (optional) |
| **Cross-curricular links** | ● D&T: making food; creating menus<br>● PSHE: financial awareness; healthy eating | ● Literacy: speaking and listening<br>● PSHE: financial awareness | ● Literacy: speaking and listening<br>● History: basic chronology | ● ICT: data handling<br>● PE: awareness of competitive sporting events | ● Literacy: speaking and listening<br>● D&T: designing and making<br>● PSHE: financial awareness |
| **CD-ROM material** | ● Introductory slideshow<br>● PDFs of photocopiables<br>● Blank pizza and menu templates<br>● Useful links | ● Introductory slideshow<br>● PDFs of photocopiables<br>● Harder price lists<br>● Photocopiables of headbands, wallets, maps and places | ● Introductory slideshow<br>● PDFs of photocopiables<br>● Second inventions list<br>● Harder games<br>● Blank templates<br>● Useful links | ● Introductory slideshow<br>● Random results generator<br>● PDFs of photocopiables | ● Introductory slideshow<br>● PDFs of photocopiables<br>● 2cm × 2cm planning grid<br>● Guidance on making nets |
| **Resources needed** | Photocopiables, pencils, paper; rulers, coloured pencils | Photocopiables, coloured pencils, plastic money (optional) | Multiple sets of cards and timelines photocopiables, pencils and rubbers | Photocopiables, pencils, paper; calculators (optional) | Photocopiables, pencils, paper; rulers, scissors and glue/sticky tape (optional) |
| **Timescales** | Minimum two lessons, 30 mins to one hour per lesson | Minimum two lessons, around one hour each | Minimum two lessons, around one hour each | Minimum two lessons, around one hour each | Minimum three lessons, around one hour each |
| **Organisation** | Pairs | Whole-class, pupils 'in role', lots of movement | Individual, paired or grouped for games | Individual, paired or small groups | Individual, paired or small groups |

| Ages 7–9 continued | Pages 28–31 | Pages 32–35 | Pages 36–39 | Pages 40–43 | Pages 44–47 |
|---|---|---|---|---|---|
| **Scenario** | 6. Tilemasters | 7. Castle catering | 8. Chase UK | 9. Planet power | 10. Table-top qwick cricket |
| **Focus** | Designing bespoke tiled floors, listing materials and calculating costs. | Children take on the roles of farmers providing all of the salad and vegetables for a large medieval castle. | Travelling around the UK in helicopters visiting various places as part of a race. | Create a meaningful and easy-to-understand presentation using planet data. | Pupils work in pairs or small groups to compete in a dice-based qwick cricket league. |
| **Difficulty rating (3 max.)** | ★★ | ★★★ | ★★★ | ★★★ | ★★★ |
| **Maths covered** | • Understanding shape: fractions, area, measuring, symmetry and scale<br>• Larger numbers (money)<br>• Tessellations (optional) | • Dividing by 5, 10 and 20<br>• Using calendars<br>• Fractions<br>• Presenting work clearly | • Calculating distances using larger numbers<br>• Adding time<br>• Measuring<br>• Converting using a simple scale | • Understanding and using very large numbers<br>• Rounding and estimating<br>• Data handling and interpretation | • 2-, 3-, 4- and 5-times tables (standard game up to 5 × 5, harder game up to 12 × 5)<br>• Adding TU numbers up to and over 100 |
| **Cross-curricular links** | • Art: creating designs<br>• Literacy: speaking and listening | • Literacy: speaking and listening<br>• PSHE: healthy eating | • Geography: awareness of UK geography | • Literacy: speaking and listening; reading<br>• Science: the solar system<br>• ICT: data handling | • Literacy: speaking and listening<br>• PE: awareness of different sports |
| **CD-ROM material** | • Introductory slideshow<br>• PDFs of photocopiables<br>• 1 cm × 1 cm planning grid<br>• Guidance on making tessellations | • Introductory slideshow<br>• PDFs of photocopiables<br>• Blank calendar and planning template<br>• Harder farm planning<br>• Example feast report | • Introductory slideshow<br>• PDFs of photocopiables<br>• Blank outline UK map<br>• Harder races | • Introductory slideshow<br>• PDFs of photocopiables<br>• Planet information sheets<br>• Useful links<br>• Additional materials | • Introductory slideshow<br>• PDFs of photocopiables<br>• Blank cricket ground and league table templates<br>• Guide to kwik cricket |
| **Resources needed** | Photocopiables, pencils, squared paper, rulers, shapes, coloured pencils/pens | Photocopiables, pencils, paper, coloured pencils/pens, images of vegetables (optional) | Photocopiables, pencils, paper, rulers, calculators (optional), maps (optional) | Photocopiables, pencils, paper, calculators (optional), access to solar system information | Photocopiables, pencils, paper, dice, league table (on CD-ROM) |
| **Timescales** | Minimum three lessons, around one hour each | Minimum two lessons, around one hour each | Minimum two lessons, around one hour each | Minimum three lessons, around one hour each | Minimum two lessons, around one hour each |
| **Organisation** | Pairs or small groups | Small groups | Small groups | Pairs or small groups | Pairs or small groups, rotating regularly |

# Pizza please!

## Overview

This is a straightforward activity to get children used to the style of *Real-Life Maths* activities. In this activity they create pizzas to order, read charts and calculate costs.

## Timescales

- Lesson 1 (30 minutes): Introduce the children to the scenario and concepts and work through some examples.
- Lesson 2 (approximately 1 hour): Children create and cost a range of pizzas, then compare each other's work.
- Further lessons: Lessons can be repeated using different orders, and with children creating their own orders.
- Extension: Ask the children to bring in take-away menus and compare them. Challenge them to design and create their own pizza menu (see *Useful pizza links* for ideas). *Pizza menu template* can be used as a writing frame.

## Maths covered

Reading charts; calculating costs; basic fractions; adding numbers up to 20 (and beyond).

## Prior learning

Children will need an understanding of simple fractions, money and number bonds up to 20.

## Cross-curricular links

- Design and technology: making food; creating menus.
- PSHE: financial awareness; healthy eating.

## CD-ROM resources list

- Scenario video and slideshow.
- Photocopiables: *Scenario guidelines, Customer orders, Ingredients charts, Pizza templates, Useful pizza links, Pizza menu template.*

## Resources list

Pencils, paper, rulers, coloured pencils.

## Setting the scene

Show the children the introduction on the CD-ROM. Explain that they will be taking the roles of staff in a take-away pizza restaurant. Work through the *Scenario guidelines* and discuss how groups should try to organise and present their work via some examples. Be sure to cover both how to work out the costs (using *Ingredients charts*) and shade the fractions appropriately on the paper pizzas (see *Pizza templates*).

## Running the scenario

Arrange the children in pairs. Explain that they can either divide roles – one making pizzas and the other calculating costs – or share them. Either give pairs the same orders from *Customer orders* and then compare their work, or give different pairs different orders. If the orders become too hard, make up new orders for the children. Decide what pace the lesson runs at: use the slideshow on an interactive whiteboard (IWB) to announce new orders; distribute photocopies; or simply read out orders at the pace that best suits.

## Differentiation

**Less confident learners** could work on the easier orders, focusing on either creating the paper pizzas or the calculations. **More confident learners** might work alone, or focus on the harder orders. They might also be encouraged to calculate mentally, and even be challenged to give change for customers handing in £10, £20, £30 and so on.

## Review

Allow the children to share their work with each other, and then have one or more groups present to the class. Are the children's pizzas correct? Is the work clearly presented and easy to understand? Would the customers be happy with their pizzas? Would the children enjoy another session where the pace of orders is increased?

## Further ideas

- Arrange for the class to visit a pizza restaurant, or have a chef visit. If practical, allow them to make their own pizzas.
- Alternatively, once the children have designed their own pizza menus (see Extension), role play restaurant visits with some of the class as paying customers. See *Useful pizza links* for recipes and further information on pizzas.
- Provide information as to what constitutes a healthy diet, including salt and fat consumption. Look at pizza ingredient lists. Are pizzas acceptable as part of a healthy diet?
- Set up a pizza take-away in the classroom with two children working behind the counter. In rotation, the rest of the children come up to place their orders. Include handing over money and giving change.

Welcome to *Pizza please!* the pizza house with a difference. Not only can you choose all your own ingredients, you can choose how much of the pizza they go on! Perfect for sharing – you like tomato, I like mushrooms, no problemo!

Or if you want it all for yourself, that's no problem either – just say what you want and we'll put it on the top, pronto!

Pizza Please!

## Rules for making pizzas

- Simple – always give customers what they want!
- Create a small model of your pizza on paper to show what it would look like.

## Calculating costs

- Different pizza bases cost different amounts.
- Use the *Ingredients charts* photocopiable to calculate the costs.

## Example

- A customer would like a small pizza, half covered with mushrooms and half onions.

One small pizza   = £6
½ mushrooms     = £2
½ onions         = £2
Total cost of pizza = £10

- Use this fraction pizza as a guide to help you make your own pizzas.

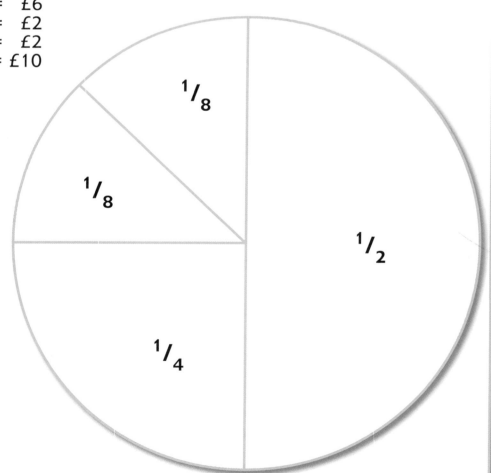

# Customer orders — Pizza please!

## Single-pizza orders

**1** **One small pizza**
Half mushrooms, half olives.

**2** **One large pizza, to share between two**
These customers would like a large pizza to share: half mushrooms, half ham.

**3** **One king-size pizza, to share between four**
Half onions, one quarter mushrooms, one eighth sweetcorn, one eighth olives.

**4** **One medium pizza**
Half asparagus, one quarter olives, one eighth sweetcorn, one eighth plain.

## Larger orders

**5** **Two medium pizzas**
Pizza 1: half sweetcorn, half onions.
Pizza 2: half olives, one quarter mushrooms, one quarter sweetcorn.

**6** **Three small pizzas**
Pizza 1: half mushrooms, half sweetcorn.
Pizza 2: half onion, half pepperoni.
Pizza 3: half pepperoni, half sweetcorn.

**7** **Two king-size pizzas with double toppings!**
Pizza 1: whole mushrooms AND half pepperoni, half asparagus.
Pizza 2: whole sweetcorn AND half olives, one quarter ham, one quarter plain.

**8** **One large and one small pizza**
Large pizza: half onions, half sweetcorn.
Small pizza: half onions, one quarter olives and one quarter ham.

## More complicated orders

**9** **Two small pizzas**
Pizza 1: half olives, half pepperoni.
Pizza 2: one quarter olives, one quarter asparagus, one quarter sweetcorn, one quarter plain.

**10** **One small, one medium, one large and one king-size pizza, all with double toppings!**
All four pizzas: cover with mushrooms, then half olives, half asparagus.

**11** **Three medium pizzas**
For a birthday surprise! Please select any toppings of your choice.
Maximum cost = £30.

**12** **Two king-size pizzas (for an awkward customer)**
Both the same: one third mushrooms, one third asparagus, one sixth ham, one sixth plain.
(Can you work out the appropriate prices for the ingredients?)

REAL-LIFE MATHS Ages 7–9 Scenario 1

# Ingredients charts — Pizza please!

| Pizza size | Cost |
|---|---|
| small | £6 |
| medium | £8 |
| large | £10 |
| king-size | £12 |

*(All pizzas include cheese and tomato topping.)*

| Ingredients | Cost per $1/_8$ | Cost per $1/_4$ | Cost per $1/_2$ | Cost for whole |
|---|---|---|---|---|
| mushrooms | 50p | £1 | £2 | £4 |
| onions | 50p | £1 | £2 | £4 |
| sweetcorn | 50p | £1 | £2 | £4 |
| olives | 50p | £1 | £2 | £4 |
| asparagus | 75p | £1.50 | £3 | £6 |
| ham | 75p | £1.50 | £3 | £6 |
| pepperoni | 75p | £1.50 | £3 | £6 |

*Do your calculations below. (For example: one small pizza, whole covered with mushrooms = £6 + £4 = £10.)*

**Order:**

**Order:**

**Order:**

**Order:**

**Order:**

**Order:**

Continue on the other side if necessary

# Tumbletown

## Overview

The children take on the roles of tourists and rickshaw drivers, the tourists paying the rickshaw drivers fares to visit a range of attractions in Tumbletown.

## Timescales

- Lesson 1 (1 hour): Introduce concepts and guidelines; assign roles and work through some examples.
- Lesson 2 (at least 1 hour): Run a full 'tourist day' and check the children's work.
- Further lessons (at least 1 hour): Repeat the previous lesson but assign different roles.
- Extension: Challenge the children to repeat the day using the photocopiables *Harder fares* and *Hardest fares* and/ or ask them to keep track of their time.

## Maths covered

Adding and subtracting to 20, 50 or 100; money; time (optional).

## Cross-curricular links

- Literacy: speaking and listening.
- PSHE: financial awareness.

## CD-ROM resources list

- Scenario video and slideshow.
- Photocopiables: *Scenario guidelines, Rickshaw driver's guide, Tourist's guide, Tumbletown tourist map, Armband and wallet, Coins, Tourist's guide – Harder fares/Hardest fares, Rickshaw driver's guide – Harder fares/Hardest fares,* 10 Tumbletown tourist attraction sheets.

## Resources list

Coloured pencils, Tumbletown money (using the *Coins* photocopiable from the CD-ROM) or a wide range of plastic coins.

## Setting the scene

Watch the introduction on the CD-ROM. Discuss the idea of visiting places and sightseeing. Familiarise the children with the roles and rules outlined in the *Scenario guidelines*. Provide each child with a *Tumbletown tourist map*. Discuss using taxis and rickshaws to get around. Work through some examples of paying fares and giving change, using small amounts.

## Running the scenario

- Think about how to arrange the learning space – there will be lots of movement. Ideally use a space with limited furniture; otherwise the activity can be done sitting in groups, with the journeys all being imaginary.

- Around 60 per cent of the class should be tourists, on their own or in pairs; the other 40 per cent should be rickshaw drivers; provide the children with a copy of *Rickshaw driver's guide* or *Tourist's guide* as appropriate.
- Ensure the children understand the rules that govern the roles. Discuss appropriate behaviour to avoid accidents: rickshaw drivers should walk at all times; 'driving' someone can be signified by holding hands or holding onto the back of a partner's sweatshirt.
- Ensure that the children can easily identify rickshaw drivers (create armbands or headbands using the templates on *Armband and wallet*).
- Give out or cut out coins as indicated on the *Tourist's/ Rickshaw driver's guide*. Keeping hold of money may be a problem for children. Ideally they should have little wallets made of paper (see the template on *Armband and wallet*).
- Print out the 10 tourist attraction sheets (*The Big Wheel, The Golden Palace* and so on). Stick them up around the space, ideally in the same order that they appear on the map. Leave pencils at each attraction for the children to use to tick or colour their maps.
- Children may find themselves short of change. They should be encouraged to get change from one another, but if that is not possible the teacher can act as a bank, providing change (not extra money) for those needing it.

## Differentiation

**Less confident learners** can work in pairs.
**More confident learners** should be encouraged to track their time (see *Scenario guidelines*) or use one of the more challenging photocopiable sheets from the CD-ROM.

## Review

At the end of the 'day' allow the children five minutes or so to add up their takings or to check their spending and change. Which rickshaw driver took the most money? Why? Discuss how the day unfolded and how the children might act differently next time.

## Further ideas

- Challenge the children to create their own versions of Tumbletown, working in groups to create their own maps and lists of rickshaw fares.
- Provide children with copies of local bus times and fares and ask them to plan a day out for the class.

The glorious town of Tumbletown, with its marvellous attractions and streets buzzing with rickshaws. Rickshaws are sometimes pedal-operated, sometimes motorised, but always fun and convenient! Tumbletown is unusual – look at the map! There is a roundabout in the centre with a road going to each attraction. Tumbletown is so unusual that tourists come from far and wide! Would you like to visit Tumbletown?

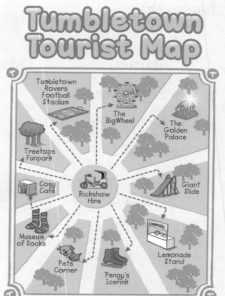

### Tourists

- Start where you like – at the centre or by an attraction – and wait your turn when queuing for rickshaws.

- You must get a rickshaw to each attraction. Pay the driver before you start your journey. Your driver will lead you to the attraction and then leave you there.

- Once you get to the attraction, tick or colour it on your map.

- Then get a rickshaw from the attraction back to the centre of town, and wait to get another rickshaw to the next attraction. *You cannot travel to an attraction and back to the centre of town using the same rickshaw.*

- Keep going until you have visited every attraction and returned to the centre.

### Rickshaw drivers

- Start anywhere you like but remember to wait your turn behind other drivers.

- Once you get to a place you must wait there until you get a new customer. *You cannot take the same customer back from that attraction to the centre.*

- If you arrive at an attraction and another tourist is waiting you can take them back to town for the correct fare.

### Running out of change

If you find you have run out of change, either ask someone else for change or go to the teacher, who is running a bank, and get them to change your money for you.

### Timekeeping

If your teacher suggests it, tourists must keep track of their time in Tumbletown throughout the day. Write what time you want your day to start at the top of your sheet (this doesn't have to match the real time or anyone else's time). Instead of ticking an attraction when you get there, write the time you arrive there, and at the very end write what time you finish. You must imagine:

- All journeys take 5 minutes.
- You stay at every attraction for 10 minutes.
- If you have to wait for a rickshaw, add on another 5 minutes.

Name(s)_____

| Attractions | One-way fares |
|---|---|
| The Big Wheel | 1p |
| The Golden Palace | 2p |
| Cosy Café | 3p |
| Tumbletown Rovers Football Stadium | 4p |
| Pets Corner | 5p |
| Lemonade Stand | 6p |
| Giant Slide | 7p |
| Pengy's Ice Rink | 8p |
| Museum of Socks | 9p |
| Treetops Funpark | 10p |

■ All rickshaw drivers start with a float of 40p in change: by the end of the day you should have much more!

**Name(s)**_____

- Remember to tick each attraction when you have been there.

| Attraction | Visited? |
|---|---|
| The Big Wheel | |
| The Golden Palace | |
| Cosy Café | |
| Tumbletown Rovers Football Stadium | |
| Pets Corner | |
| Lemonade Stand | |
| Giant Slide | |
| Pengy's Ice Rink | |
| Museum of Socks | |
| Treetops Funpark | |

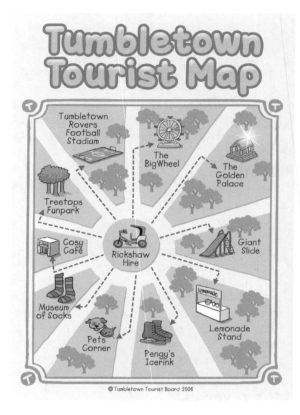

Tumbletown Tourist Map

© Tumbletown Tourist Board 2006

- All tourists start with £2: by the end of the day you should have much less!

# A brief history of inventions

## Overview

In this activity children put a range of inventions into date order. The activity provides practice and reinforcement of ordering numbers between 1000 and 2000. Please note that precisely dating some inventions can be difficult, and different sources may well provide dates different from those in the scenario's main activity.

## Timescales

- Lesson 1 (approximately 1 hour): Introduce timelines, the games to be played and rules, and reinforce the children's understanding of place value up to 2000.
- Lesson 2 (approximately 1 hour): Play the game(s) in full.
- Further lessons: A second playing of the games may be easier. Introducing children to harder levels will challenge them further (see the photocopiable sheet *Harder invention games*). There is also another set of inventions on the photocopiable sheet *Victorians to the present*.
- Extension: Challenge children who can handle the calculations to try the hardest game: 20/20 (see the photocopiable sheet *Harder invention games*).

## Maths covered

Ordering numbers between 1000 and 2000; using knowledge of number bonds to 20 to solve problems with larger numbers (extension).

## Prior learning

Children should be familiar with place value up to at least 2000.

## Cross-curricular links

- Literacy: speaking and listening.
- History: basic chronology.

## CD-ROM resources list

- Scenario video and slideshow.
- Photocopiables: *Scenario guidelines, Invention dates, Date recording sheet, Harder invention games, Inventions, Blank inventions sheet, Blank timeline, Victorians to the present, Useful invention links.*

## Resources list

Pencils and rubbers, multiple sets of invention cards and timelines made from *Invention dates* and *Date-recording sheet* (if possible, mount and laminate the invention cards).

## Setting the scene

Explain to the class that they will be playing a range of games working with larger numbers, placing them in order according to the dates that a selection of items were first invented. Discuss how, logically, some inventions must come before others (for example, the wheel was invented before the car), and watch the introduction on the CD-ROM. Using simple examples from the school day or year, and then moving on to significant dates (such as birthdays) reinforce the children's understanding of simple timelines and chronology. With a level of game in mind, display *Scenario guidelines* or *Harder invention games* and discuss the rules. Model how to play some or all of the games, using the *Date recording sheet* and *Invention dates*.

## Running the scenario

All the games require two players or teams. If the children are secure with the gameplay and rules the games should work well. It is advisable to group partners and opponents who can work at a similar level. Distribute one *Date recording sheet* per player or team, and a set of invention cards for each pair of players or teams. Circulate the class during play and remind children of the rules as appropriate.

## Differentiation

There are four game levels detailed in the *Scenario guidelines* and on *Harder invention games*; placing children in pairings or teams of similar ability will enable them to work at an appropriate level.

## Review

After each game gather the class together and ask if they experienced any difficulties. Discuss the difference between saying dates (for example, *seventeen thirty-two*) and their numbers (*one thousand, seven hundred and thirty-two*).

## Further ideas

- Create new timeline games using *Inventions* and *Blank inventions sheet*.
- Focus on inventions – ask the children to research the inventors of certain items, adding their details to a class timeline (see *Blank timeline* and *Useful invention links*).
- Focus on time – focus on a particular topic, such as travel or communication, and produce timelines for it. Can the children use their maths to calculate how many years elapsed between each invention?
- Create a timeline display from the work produced.

We live in a world of inventions – things created by humans that (usually) make our lives better and easier. Some ancient inventions such as the wheel are still used today, and recent inventions such as the internet can really change the way we live. It is interesting to think about how inventions come about – often because of clever people and other inventions that come before them.

## Rules for all 'inventions' games

- The winner is the first player (or team of players) to complete their timeline.
- For every game you will need: 24 invention cards, a blank timeline for each player.
- Shuffle all the invention cards and put them face down on the table.
- Each player should take eight cards and keep them safe, without showing the other player, leaving eight cards on the table.
- Turn over the eight cards on the table and arrange them in chronological order with the oldest invention at the top. Both players can enter these eight dates and the dates of the eight inventions in their hand onto their own timeline, estimating where the inventions are placed if they are not exactly sure.
- *Note – you may have to change objects' places on the timeline, so use a pencil.*

## Game 1 – Before or after? (introductory level)

- Agree who's going to go first. This player then chooses an invention on one of their own cards and asks: *Was the [1] invented before or after the [2]?* Where [1] is any card in their hand and [2] is any card on the table.
- If the other player answers correctly, the first player must put the [1] card on the table, in the correct place. The other player enters the date onto their timeline.
- If the player answers incorrectly, the first player keeps the card.
- It is now the other player's turn. Keep going until one player has completed their timeline. They can declare that they are finished, but they have only won if their timeline has been completed correctly.

## Game 2 – True or false? (standard level)

- Players must make a 'true' or 'false' statement based on one of their cards, such as: *The telephone was invented in 1876* (true); or *The telephone was invented in 1985* (false). The answering player must decide if the statement is true or false, with the same results as in 'Before or after?' for a correct or incorrect answer.
- *Note – this game relies on everyone being honest. No cheating allowed!*

# Invention dates — A brief history of inventions

| | | | |
|---|---|---|---|
| printing press  1437 | hot-air balloon  1783 | aeroplane  1903 | satellite navigation ('sat nav')  1985 |
| encyclopaedia  1751 | telephone  1876 | contact lens  1887 | candle clock  1206 |
| ballpoint pen  1888 | search engine  1994 | newspaper  1605 | compass  1090 |
| telescope  1668 | personal computer  1968 | postage stamp  1840 | spectacles  1315 |
| pencil  1795 | mobile phone  1973 | sextant  1757 | pocket watch  1504 |
| email  1971 | microscope  1615 | photocopier  1938 | typewriter  1873 |

# Date recording sheet — A brief history of inventions

| Date | Invention |
|---|---|
| | 1000–1099 |
| | |
| | 1100–1299 |
| | |
| | 1300–1399 |
| | |
| | 1400–1499 |
| | |
| | 1500–1599 |
| | |
| | 1600–1699 |
| | |
| | |
| | 1700–1799 |
| | |
| | |
| | |
| | |
| | 1800–1899 |
| | |
| | |
| | |
| | |
| | |
| | 1900–1999 |
| | |
| | |
| | |
| | |
| | |
| | |
| | |
| | 2000 (can you think of any inventions after this date?) |
| | |

- Add the names of some objects and the date each one was invented to this table to create a timeline.

- Date ranges have been entered to help you.

## Teacher notes

# School sports day

## Overview

Children take part in a virtual sports day, monitoring competitors' progress through a range of typical sports day events. They must then check each other's work, awarding or deducting points for correct/incorrect calculations.

## Timescales

- Lesson 1 (approximately 1 hour): Introduce the events and the scoring system via some examples.
- Lesson 2 (at least 1 hour): Complete all events in the virtual sports day then check each other's work; calculate final scores; decide on the winner.
- Further lessons: Competitors' results change each time you use the CD-ROM. Try reducing calculation time.
- Extension: Provide the children with a copy of *Sample data*; challenge them to calculate the final points for all competitors *and* calculate team points.

## Maths covered

Using simple formulae; multiplying and dividing larger numbers by 2; subtracting one- and two-digit numbers from 50; adding multiple one- and two-digit numbers to over 100; checking work with a calculator.

## Prior learning

Children will need to be confident multiplying and dividing by 2, and adding and subtracting two-digit numbers.

## Cross-curricular links

- ICT: data handling.
- PE: awareness of competitive sporting events.

## CD-ROM resources list

- Scenario video and slideshow.
- On-screen results generator.
- Photocopiables: *Scenario guidelines, Scorecard, Sample data.*

## Resources list

Pencils, paper, calculators (optional, for checking work).

## Setting the scene

Show the class the introductory video on the CD-ROM and discuss their understanding of sports days. Explain that they will be taking part in a virtual sports day, selecting a competitor and following their progress. Distribute or display the *Scenario guidelines* and talk through the activities and how scores are calculated. Work through a sample calculation for each type of event: racing, throwing and

jumping. In particular, point out that for the jumping events remainders can be ignored. Also point out that for the racing events subtraction is required to give those who finish fastest the most points. Distribute *Scorecard* and talk through how it works, reminding the children that they must only complete the first two columns during the events.

## Running the scenario

- Arrange children individually, in pairs or in small groups, as desired. As there are nine competitors taking part, either arrange nine groups or have some children choosing the same competitor (the final scoring system still allows for different results). Ask the children to name their competitor, then start the sports day on your IWB (or use *Sample data* if no IWB is available). As the scenario runs, check that the children are comfortable calculating points for each event, pausing as required.
- Once all nine events have been completed the children must check each other's calculations (with a calculator if desired). You may need to arbitrate for disagreements. The scorecard has space for children to certify whether calculations are correct or not, and then award or deduct additional points appropriately. Once finished, collate everyone's scores and decide on which competitors have won gold, silver and bronze. If you wish to extend the work, ask more confident children to calculate the team awards (red, green and blue).

## Differentiation

**Less confident learners** should use a pencil and paper to make their calculations.
**More confident learners** could calculate mentally.

## Review

Once all work has been checked and agreed on, create a final scorecard for all the class to see. Do the children think that the points system is fair? What would have happened if points had been given as 1 for last, 2 for second last and so on for each event – would the results have been different?

## Further ideas

Children could plan an actual sports day of their own, either for themselves or for younger children, using events of their choice and suitable formulae for each event.

In this virtual school sports day you must watch the results for imaginary competitors taking part in nine events, and calculate the number of points awarded to each competitor for each event.

Afterwards the points are added up and the highest total is the winner.

Beware! You can lose points for incorrect calculations, and gain points for good maths.

## Rules for participating

- You must choose a virtual competitor at the start of the 'day' and stick with them.

- You must carefully calculate your competitor's points after each event. (See *Scorecard* for instructions on how to calculate points.)

- After the last event you must swap work with someone else and check each other's work.

- Competitors *gain* an extra 10 points for every correct calculation, but *lose* 10 points for every incorrect calculation.

- If you are checking someone else's score and you think it is incorrect, you must recalculate the score with them. If you both agree that the answer is incorrect, write down what their score should have been, remembering to take away 10 points.

## School sports day events

- **40-metre sprint** – how quickly the competitor can run 40 metres; measured in seconds (s).

- **Standing jump** – how far the competitor can jump from standing still; measured in centimetres (cm).

- **Tennis ball toss** – how far the competitor can throw a tennis ball underarm; measured in metres (m).

- **High jump** – how high the competitor can jump; measured in centimetres (cm).

- **Bouncy-hopper race** – how quickly the competitor can bounce 25 metres; measured in seconds (s).

- **Welly wanging** – how far the competitor can throw a welly; measured in metres (m).

- **Long hop** – how far the competitor can go in a single hop; measured in centimetres (cm).

- **Foam javelin throw** – how far the competitor can throw a foam javelin; measured in metres (m).

- **Sack race** – how quickly the competitor can jump 25 metres in a sack; measured in seconds (s).

**Your name(s):**_____   **Team:**_____

**Competitor number:**_____   **Competitor name:**_____

| Event | Time/ distance | Points scored | Checked (right or wrong?) | + or − 10 points | Final points scored |
|---|---|---|---|---|---|
| 40-metre sprint | | | | | |
| Standing jump | | | | | |
| Tennis ball toss | | | | | |
| High jump | | | | | |
| Bouncy-hopper race | | | | | |
| Welly wanging | | | | | |
| Long hop | | | | | |
| Foam javelin throw | | | | | |
| Sack race | | | | | |
| | | | | **TOTAL POINTS:** | |

- **For *racing* activities,** measured in seconds, calculate points like this:

  50 take away the time taken = points scored.

  For example, if someone runs the 40-metre sprint in 20 seconds they score: 50 − 20 = 30 points.

- **For *throwing* activities,** measured in metres, calculate points like this:

  Distance thrown multiplied by 2 = points scored.

  For example, if someone throws the welly 5 metres they score: 5 × 2 = 10 points.

- **For *jumping* activities,** measured in centimetres, calculate points like this:

  Distance jumped divided by 2 = points scored.

  For example, if someone hops 40 centimetres they score: 40 ÷ 2 = 20 points. If someone else hops 55 centimetres they score: 55 ÷ 2 = 27 points (ignore any remainders).

- This data has been provided for those who do not have access to an interactive whiteboard. The data below represents results for nine competitors taking part. It is suggested that each set of data is presented in turn, with enough time allowed for children to calculate their chosen competitor's points.

- Please note that the software on the CD-ROM provides more variety, as all competitors' scores are calculated randomly every time the software is used.

| Competitor | 1 | 2 | 3 | 4 | 5 | 6 | 7 | 8 | 9 |
|---|---|---|---|---|---|---|---|---|---|
| **Team** | red | green | blue | red | green | blue | red | green | blue |
| 40-metre sprint (seconds) | 20 | 20 | 24 | 24 | 25 | 23 | 24 | 19 | 19 |
| Standing jump (centimetres) | 75 | 50 | 70 | 42 | 67 | 45 | 41 | 54 | 72 |
| Tennis ball toss (metres) | 20 | 17 | 17 | 19 | 16 | 17 | 16 | 17 | 17 |
| High jump (centimetres) | 47 | 49 | 55 | 47 | 60 | 44 | 53 | 46 | 68 |
| Bouncy-hopper race (seconds) | 18 | 24 | 22 | 24 | 19 | 21 | 18 | 19 | 18 |
| Welly wanging (metres) | 11 | 14 | 19 | 12 | 13 | 11 | 13 | 19 | 14 |
| Long hop (centimetres) | 42 | 50 | 43 | 59 | 60 | 46 | 52 | 60 | 57 |
| Foam javelin throw (metres) | 14 | 20 | 14 | 11 | 17 | 16 | 19 | 19 | 14 |
| Sack race (seconds) | 26 | 30 | 28 | 28 | 23 | 28 | 23 | 22 | 24 |

**Scenario 5**

# Mr Wolf's DIY shop

## Overview

By creating plans and using price lists children have to design and cost houses for the three little pigs.

## Timescales

- Lesson 1 (approximately 1 hour): Introduce the concepts and consider the skills needed. Work through an example.
- Lesson 2 (at least 1 hour): Children fully design, cost and present a house for a specific pig.
- Further lessons (at least 1 hour): Children design, cost and present houses for the other pigs.
- Extension: Using nets and modelling materials children make scale models of their houses (see the photocopiable sheet *Nets*).

## Maths covered

Choosing operations for calculating numbers up to and over 100, involving money; basic scale and measuring; simple nets (optional).

## Prior learning

Children should be comfortable with extended tasks that need careful organisation.

## Cross-curricular links

- Literacy: speaking and listening.
- Design and technology: designing and making.
- PSHE: financial awareness.

## CD-ROM resources list

- Scenario video and slideshow.
- Photocopiables: *Scenario guidelines*, *Wolfie's price list*, *Piggy profiles*, *Blank planning grid*, *Nets*.

## Resources list

Pencils, paper, rulers (optional), scissors (optional), glue or sticky tape (optional).

## Setting the scene

Explain to the class that their task will be to design and cost one or more houses for Mr Wolf's demanding customers, all of whom are (little) pigs! Use the video on the CD-ROM to meet Mr Wolf and listen to him explain what his shop sells. Introduce one or more of the customers, and then finish by looking together at the *Scenario guidelines* and *Wolfie's price list*. Discuss, model and review the different maths skills involved, as appropriate, and work through the preferred

approach to presenting work. If the children are going to draw to scale, two centimetres per metre is suggested; children can use the *Blank planning grid* from the CD-ROM.

## Running the scenario

Children can work individually, in pairs, or in small groups as desired; give each child/pair/group a copy of *Wolfie's price list* and a 'piggy profile' of your choice (see *Piggy profiles*). Everyone could have the same pig and then compare work, or different groups could have different pigs. Make sure the *Scenario guidelines* sheet is available, either on the IWB or as one copy per group. As the children work, encourage them to consider the pig's requirements carefully before starting on their plans and calculations, and remind them of the importance of the layout of their work – both in terms of design and showing costs. They will probably find it much easier to focus on one wall at a time or for each child to work on a different wall once the overall design has been decided. Remind them to include the roof!

## Differentiation

**Less confident learners** should be encouraged to design the more simpler houses and to ignore costs.
**More confident learners** should be encouraged to design the more complex houses and to provide full costs.

## Review

Depending on timescales, allow the children to share their work with each other, and then have one or more children 'pitch' or present their house to the class. Are their calculations accurate? Is their work clearly presented and easy to understand? Will the pigs be satisfied? Which house was the most expensive/cheapest?

## Further ideas

- Once the children have got the hang of the task, try asking them to design the same house out of different materials and compare the overall costs.
- Using *Nets* for guidance, ask the children to create multi-room houses and calculate costs. They should be aware that where two nets meet they need only calculate costs for one wall. Can they include internal doors, too?
- Using the nets, or the appropriate materials, create scale models of the houses, adding features as appropriate.

Welcome to my wonderful DIY shop! I do hope you can help me today. I have some new piggy customers and each one would like a new house. Can you help them to design and plan for building it?

## Rules for designing and planning

- All rooms are 3m high.
- Rooms can be any size.
- All doors are 1m wide and 2m high.
- All windows are 1m wide and 1m high.
- All panels are 1m wide and 1m high.
- Don't forget the roof and extras!

Take a look at the house below. I'm going to show you how much it costs to build the wall with the front door in.

**The wall is 4m wide and 3m high.**

**Straw panels cost £2 each.**

I drew a grid on squared paper using 2cm for every metre, and decided where to put the door and the window. Then I worked out we need:

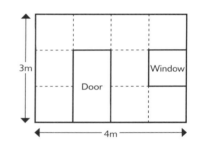

| | | |
|---|---|---|
| **9 straw panels at £2 each** | = | **£18** |
| **1 straw door at £5 each** | = | **£5** |
| **One window at £4 each** | = | **£4** |
| **Cost for front wall** | = | **£27** |

After that it was easy to work out the cost for all the other walls and the roof by drawing grids for each one:

Both side walls are 2m wide by 3m high, with no windows: **so 6 panels each.**

The back wall is 4m long by 3m high, no windows: **that's 12 panels.**

The roof is 4m long by 2m wide: **that's 8 panels.**

Then I added on a false chimney.
**(Straw chimneys cost £10 each.)**

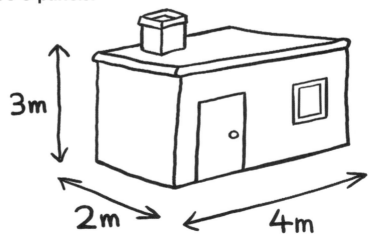

**Total cost:**

| | | | |
|---|---|---|---|
| **Front wall** | | = | **£27** |
| **Side wall 1** | = £2 × 6 | = | **£12** |
| **Side wall 2** | = £2 × 6 | = | **£12** |
| **Back wall** | = £2 × 12 | = | **£24** |
| **Roof** | = £2 × 8 | = | **£16** |
| **Chimney** | | = | **£10** |
| **Total** | | = | **£101** |

## Wall panels (all panels are 1m wide and 1m high)

| Straw | Sticks | Stone | Plastic | Metal |
|---|---|---|---|---|
| £2 per panel | £3 per panel | £4 per panel | £5 per panel | £10 per panel |

 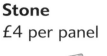  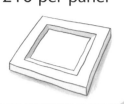

## Doors (all doors are 1m wide and 2m high)

| Straw | Sticks | Stone | Plastic | Metal |
|---|---|---|---|---|
| £5 per door | £10 per door | £15 per door | £20 per door | £40 per door |

  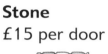  

## Windows (all windows are 1m wide and 1m high)

| Straw frames | Stick frames | Stone frames | Plastic frames | Metal frames |
|---|---|---|---|---|
| £4 per window | £6 per window | £8 per window | £10 per window | £20 per window |

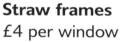 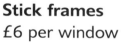   

## Extras

| Wolf Alarm | Curtains |
|---|---|
| £15 each | £25 per pair |

| | False chimney | Porch |
|---|---|---|
| Straw | £10 each | £20 each |
| Sticks | £20 each | £40 each |
| Stone | £30 each | £60 each |
| Plastic | £40 each | £80 each |
| Metal | £80 each | £160 each |

### Little Pig 1

I just love straw. I'm not very strong so it will be easy for me to build a house with straw. I'll only need one large room, and I would be most grateful if I could have a wolf alarm!

Remember:

- All rooms should be 3m high.
- All doors are 1m wide and 2m high.
- All windows are 1m wide and 1m high.
- Don't forget the roof!

### Little Pig 2

Sticks please! I want a house all of my own, made of sticks! One room is fine, but please give me a wolf alarm and curtains.

Remember:

- All rooms should be 3m high.
- All doors are 1m wide and 2m high.
- All windows are 1m wide and 1m high.
- Don't forget the roof!

### Little Pig 3

I'd like a house built of stone please. I'll need one large room and one small room just in case I have guests. I think a chimney may come in handy too.

Remember:

- All rooms should be 3m high.
- All doors are 1m wide and 2m high.
- All windows are 1m wide and 1m high.
- Don't forget the roof!

### Mrs Pig

Being a mother is never easy. I really don't want my little darlings to leave home, but my cottage is just so small. What would be perfect is a nice house big enough for all four of us, and of course strong enough to keep the wolf away!

I'd be happy with a bungalow or a two-storey house, as long as it has at least two bedrooms, and all the latest features – an alarm, curtains, chimney and porch.

Remember:

- All rooms should be 3m high.
- All doors are 1m wide and 2m high.
- All windows are 1m wide and 1m high.
- Don't forget the roof!

# Tilemasters

## Overview

In this activity children design bespoke tiled floors according to specified requirements. They list the amounts of different tile types required for each floor and calculate the cost of the materials used.

## Timescales

- Lesson 1 (approximately 1 hour): Introduce the class to the scenario and work through an example.
- Lesson 2 (at least 1 hour): Children design a specific floor, list materials and present costs.
- Further lessons: Children design and cost a range of floors for multiple customers.
- Extension: Children create their own bespoke customer orders, possibly involving tessellations. They then create appropriate designs and provide costings for their work.

## Maths covered

Understanding shape: fractions, area, measuring, symmetry, simple scale and tessellations (optional); multiplying and adding larger numbers; money: calculating costs.

## Prior learning

Children will need an understanding of simple shapes, fractions, symmetry and addition and multiplication of two- and three-digit numbers.

## Cross-curricular links

- Art: creating designs.
- Literacy: speaking and listening.

## CD-ROM resources list

- Scenario video and slideshow.
- Photocopiables: *Scenario guidelines*, *Order list*, *Design proposal*, *Blank grid*, *Tiles and tessellations*.

## Resources list

Pencils, squared paper (or use *Blank grid*), rulers, assorted shapes, coloured pencils or pens.

## Setting the scene

Show the film clips and slideshow of photographs relating to mosaics on the CD-ROM. Discuss the children's understanding of tiles and consider the work needed to make tiled floors. Explain to the class that they will be taking the role of floor designers: each group or pair will receive an order, and they must organise the work between themselves, producing draft designs and listing the materials required. Work through the *Scenario guidelines* and discuss how the

children should try to plan and present their work. If necessary, cover methods of working to scale and work through an example order from *Order list* together. Pay particular attention to costings and how to multiply by 20, 30 and so on. If appropriate, cover converting pence to pounds.

## Running the scenario

Arrange the children in pairs or small groups and allocate an order to each group. Everyone could have the same order and then compare work, or different groups could have different orders. Ensure copies of the *Design proposal* and *Blank grid* (or sheets of squared paper) are available. Remind the children about the key factors in planning the floor: colour schemes, scale, symmetry and so on. Encourage them to spend time brainstorming ideas and discussing issues, and encourage them to carefully consider the requirements of their specific order, in particular planning the design (on squared paper, one square per tile) before starting any calculations.

## Differentiation

**Less confident learners** should work only on the design, specifying shapes and features.
**More confident learners** can develop more complex designs, leading to accurate listings of materials and ultimately costings for the whole floor. They could also consider how to fulfil the order and keep costs to a minimum.

## Review

Allow children to share their work with each other, and then have one or more groups present to the class. Have they met the customers' expectations? Are their calculations for material requirements accurate? Is the work clearly presented and easy to understand? Would the clients agree to their designs?

## Further ideas

- Create a life-size wall or floor display of the children's designs using coloured paper or something similar.
- More confident children could look at tessellating patterns (see *Tiles and tessellations* on the CD-ROM) and design a tiled floor in this style.
- ICT – use the computer to create intricate tile designs and then repeat them.

You will be working as a designer for a company that designs tiled floors. (In hotter countries it is common to have tiled floors throughout the house, and although the UK can be cold tiled floors are becoming popular here too.) The reputation of the company depends on the good work you produce, so make sure you give the customers what they want.

## Rules for designing and planning

- Tiles are always 10cm by 10cm. So, ten complete tiles will equal 1m in length.
- Tiles can be cut in straight lines in any direction, including diagonally.
- If you do cut tiles, try to use the spare bits too, as you have to add up costs for all tiles.
- Draw your designs on squared paper, with one square representing one tile.

## Presenting your work

- Draw a plan of the floor on squared paper, using one square per tile.
- On your *Design proposal*, say briefly *why* you think the customer will like your work.

## Calculating costs

- Show your calculations next to your costings and be sure to give an overall cost for your design.
- Different-coloured tiles cost different amounts. There is a chart for this on your *Design proposal* sheet.
- For unusual shapes you may have to cut tiles.

## Tips for effective working

- If you are working in a group make sure everyone has something to do and that you all agree on your plans.
- If possible, look at lots of examples of tiled floors before you start.
- Start by drawing the outline of the floor, and check with your teacher that the scale is correct.
- Try sketching lots of ideas in rough and experiment with different colours.
- Don't waste time colouring in your ideas – save that for your final design, or use coloured paper.
- Calculate the number of tiles used by counting the squares on your design.

**Straightforward designs**

**1** **Square floor, 1m wide by 1m long**
The customer would like a checked pattern using only two colours: half orange, half red.

**2** **Square floor, 2m wide by 2m long**
The customer would like a border, with a pattern using darker colours surrounding a bright pattern.

**3** **Rectangular floor, 1m wide by 2m long**
The customer would like a symmetrical pattern using as many different-coloured tiles as you wish.

**4** **Rectangular floor, 1m wide by 3m long**
The customer would like a repeating pattern, with a third of the floor for each colour.

**More complex designs**

**5** **Square floor, 2m wide by 2m long**
The customer would like a diagonally repeating pattern, with one third of the tiles green, one third blue and one third yellow.

**6** **Square floor, 1m by 1m**
The customer would like a pattern of your choice, using three colours. Half the tiles must be one colour, one quarter another colour, and one quarter a third colour.

**7** **Square floor, 2m by 2m**
The customer would like a beautiful design, with a checked border and a centre pattern made using triangular tiles only.

**8** **Rectangular floor, 2m wide by 4m long**
The customer would like a white floor with blue tiles spelling out a word across the middle.

**Open designs for greater creativity**

**9** **Rectangular floor, 1m wide by 2m long**
The customer would like a design made using triangular tiles in whatever style you prefer, maybe using the colours of the rainbow.

**10** **Square floor, 2m by 2m**
The customer would love a symmetrical pattern, with at least two lines of symmetry, made using blue, red and green tiles.

**11** **Huge square floor, 4m by 4m**
The customer would like the floor divided into four sections, each part representing a different season of the year.

**12** **Circular floor, 1m in diameter**
The customer would like a symmetrical pattern radiating from the centre, with no more than four colours. Tiles can be cut any way you want.

**Name(s)**_____

Write or stick your job details here.

■ Remember to create and present your tile designs using squared paper.

■ One square = one tile, so ten squares across = one metre.

Describe your design here, and say why you think the customer will like it.

Show your costings calculations here.

|  | Cost per tile | Number used | Total cost |
|---|---|---|---|
| white | 20p |  |  |
| red | 20p |  |  |
| blue | 30p |  |  |
| brown | 30p |  |  |
| green | 40p |  |  |
| pink | 40p |  |  |
| yellow | 50p |  |  |
| orange | 50p |  |  |
| purple | £1 |  |  |
| black | £1 |  |  |
| **Totals** |  |  |  |

# Castle catering

## Overview

In this activity children take on the roles of farmers providing all the salad and vegetables for a large medieval castle.

## Timescales

- Lesson 1 (1 hour): Introduce the scenario, consider the skills needed and work through an example event.
- Lesson 2 (at least 1 hour): Children create a full catering plan for at least two feasts and evaluate their work.
- Further lessons (at least 1 hour): Repeat for different feasts; change the salad and vegetable types (using *Farm planning – Blank template*).
- Extension: Challenge the children to plan production for the whole year, catering for all the events at the castle. They should reuse plots as appropriate. Can it be done, or will they need to rent land from neighbouring farmers for some of the time?

## Maths covered

Dividing by 5, 10 and 20; using calendars; fractions; presenting work clearly.

## Cross-curricular links

- Literacy: speaking and listening.
- PSHE: healthy eating.

## CD-ROM resources list

- Scenario video and slideshow.
- Photocopiables: *Scenario guidelines, Farm planning, Example feast report, Events for the coming year, Calendar, Farm planning – Harder version, Farm planning – Blank template*.

## Resources list

Pencils, paper, coloured pencils; images of salad and vegetables (optional).

## Setting the scene

Watch the introduction on the CD-ROM and explain to the children that they will be taking the roles of farmers supplying salad and vegetables for the feasts at Castle Grunden. Discuss the processes involved in growing food and stress that this castle is in a mythical land where growing conditions are somewhat different from our own – the climate of Grunden is consistent all the year round! Read through *Scenario guidelines* and *Farm planning* together, and work through the *Example feast report*. In particular, look at the fractions of the field that are needed for each food type and discuss how these are deduced (for example, two

sixteenths = one eighth). Stress also the use of the *Calendar* and look at how, for some, feasts planting dates will need to be calculated back to the previous year.

## Running the scenario

Arrange the children in small groups as desired. Assign two or more feasts to each group (using *Events for the coming year*), as appropriate. The six feasts available are graded in difficulty; for the first lesson it is suggested that the easiest two are used. Provide each group with at least one copy of *Farm planning*. Emphasise that the queen and king will choose a farmer for each feast based on the presentation of their reports, as well as the accuracy of their calculations. The work becomes more complicated when planning for the second feast and for the larger feasts where plots may have to be used twice. Encourage the children to sketch out their plans and monitor their calculations regularly – errors can have knock-on effects that take a long time to unpick!

## Differentiation

**Less confident learners** should work on a single feast, if necessary ignoring planting times.
**More confident learners** should be encouraged to work accurately, calculating more complex fractions and remainders; they could also use *Farm planning – Harder version*.

## Review

Give the children as much time as possible to check and share their work – this is when they realise how important presentation is. Take the part of, say, King Olarf, and decide who to choose to supply the food for your feasts, presentation, clarity and accuracy being the main deciding factors.

## Further ideas

Organise children into groups of four, assign a quarter of the year (such as January to March) to each group, and ask them to choose a date and suggest a feast for it. For example, for 14 February, Valentine's Day, 150 guests are coming and a large vegetable stew is required. Once all of the groups have written their feasts down, they reveal them to the class. Work as a class to schedule the planting and harvesting of the foods required for all the feasts. If the fields available will not provide enough, the children must calculate how much land they will need to rent from neighbouring farms.

Life in Castle Grunden is always lively. King Olarf, Queen Beatrice and their family are big food lovers, but they are healthy with it. They receive only the best supplies from the local butchers and fishmongers, and salad and vegetables from their favourite farmers. You are one of these farmers – will they choose you to provide their food for this year's feasts?

## Your farm

- In the kingdom of Grunden all foods grow well all year round. Paradise!
- You can grow a wide range of salad and vegetables on your farm.
- You have three fields.
- Each field is divided up into plots. You can grow any type of salad or vegetable on each plot.
- You can only grow one type of salad or vegetable at a time on each plot.
- You must plant food at the right time before a feast to make sure it is ready on the day of the feast.
- Each plot can grow enough food to provide ten portions.

## Providing food for a feast

- Use the *Farm planning* sheet to decide when you are going to plant the food, and in which fields.
- You may need to use more than one field for larger feasts.

## Your feast report

On plain paper, you must provide a report for King Olarf and Queen Beatrice explaining your plans to them, so that they are sure you can deliver the freshest food at the right time. Use *Example feast report* as a guide. Your report should contain the following information:

- The occasion and the date
- The number of guests
- Which foods you are going to provide
- When you will plant the seeds to make sure the food is at its freshest on the day of the feast
- Which field you will be planting each food in
- What fraction of the field the food will take up
- Whether there will be surplus food.

■ These are the different types of salad and vegetable you can grow on your farm.

## Salad

| **Lettuces** | **Cucumbers** | **Spring onions** | **Tomatoes** |
|---|---|---|---|
| Growing time: 2 months | Growing time: 3 months | Growing time: 2 months | Growing time: 3 months |
| Portions per plot: 5 | Portions per plot: 5 | Portions per plot: 10 | Portions per plot: 20 |

## Vegetables

| **Carrots** | **Cauliflowers** | **Onions** | **Parsnips** |
|---|---|---|---|
| Growing time: 3 months | Growing time: 4 months | Growing time: 5 months | Growing time: 6 months |
| Portions per plot: 20 | Portions per plot: 5 | Portions per plot: 10 | Portions per plot: 5 |
| **Courgettes** | **Cabbages** | **Broccoli** | **Potatoes** |
| Growing time: 3 months | Growing time: 4 months | Growing time: 5 months | Growing time: 6 months |
| Portions per plot: 20 | Portions per plot: 5 | Portions per plot: 5 | Portions per plot: 10 |

## Field A (16 plots)

## Field B (20 plots)

## Field C (50 plots)

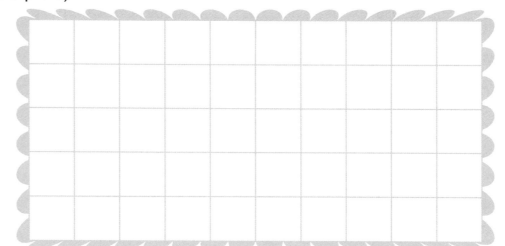

## 14 February – Queen Beatrice's birthday

Number of guests – 40

King Olarf is planning a surprise party for Queen Beatrice, with all her family invited. The butcher is providing the meat, and they would like a surprise from the farm: Beatrice loves green vegetables and pickled cucumber!

## 1 April – King Olarf's birthday

Number of guests – 50

The family is always gathered together for Olarf's birthday. He would like a tomato salad for starters, and more than anything he loves chips and carrots to go with his fish (the fishmonger is delivering the cod).

## 20 May – Prince Pickalot's birthday

Number of guests – 80

No wonder Prince Pickalot's nickname is 'Parsnip' – it's his favourite food! He also loves onions, carrots and potatoes, which the chef will chop up, add stock to, and make into an enormous cauldron of soup!

## 5 July – Grandma Grunden's 80th birthday

Number of guests – 110

Family and close friends will be invited to Grandma's party. The castle chef has been instructed to prepare a green salad of cucumber, spring onions and lettuce for starters, with cauliflower cheese for the main course.

## 20 October – Princess Dearheart's wedding

Number of guests – 125

The event of the year, without a doubt, is Princess Dearheart's marriage to the dashing Prince Norbert. The wedding feast must be impressive – all of Norbert's family are coming and they love baked potatoes, courgettes and carrots cooked in butter.

The castle chef would also like a mixture of all your salad items for the starters.

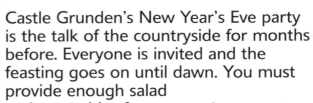

## 31 December – New Year's Eve

Number of guests – 175

Castle Grunden's New Year's Eve party is the talk of the countryside for months before. Everyone is invited and the feasting goes on until dawn. You must provide enough salad and vegetables for everyone to have two big meals!

# Chase UK

## Overview

Children must imagine they are racing to various places around the UK in helicopters. They must calculate distances and journey times. There are four different games with increasing levels of difficulty.

## Timescales

- Lesson 1 (approximately 1 hour): Introduce the event and the maths concepts. Work in small groups or as a class to plan a strategy and route for the quick race.
- Lesson 2 (at least 1 hour): Run the race and check workings.
- Further lessons: Repeat the race, either at a harder level or using different starting points or routes.
- Extension: Children use online or printed maps to make other races (for example, visit six castles across the UK) and challenge classmates to complete them. They mark the relevant places on the *Blank UK map*.

## Maths covered

Calculating distances using larger numbers; adding time; measuring; converting distances using a simple scale.

## Prior learning

Children should be able to read and calculate time by adding on minutes and have an understanding of adding larger numbers up to 1000.

## Cross-curricular links

Geography: awareness of UK geography.

## CD-ROM resources list

- Scenario video and slideshow.
- Photocopiables: *Scenario guidelines, UK map, Race recording sheet, Blank UK map, Harder challenges.*

## Resources list

Pencils, paper, rulers, calculators (optional), maps (optional).

## Setting the scene

Discuss UK geography as desired (there is a map on the CD-ROM that can be displayed or distributed), in particular checking children's basic understanding of the different countries within the UK and the existence of capital cities for each one. Show the introductory film and *UK map* on your IWB, and explain that the children will be competing in a helicopter race around the UK. Display or distribute the *Scenario guidelines* explaining the rules of the race, and stress that racers must stop in both John O'Groats and

Land's End. Emphasise that they cannot travel further than 200 miles without refuelling, and work through a sample journey to show their considerations involved in planning and recording, in particular focusing on how to multiply to convert map measurements into miles (1cm = 25 miles; 1mm = 2.5 miles).

## Running the scenario

Organise the children in small groups. Decide on the level of difficulty the children should work at, and give each group a copy of the *UK map* and a *Race recording sheet*. Ensure that all children have set themselves an appropriate starting point and know the requirements of the race they are working on. Throughout the task remind the children that all work will be checked at the end and any errors mean disqualification. To increase tension, set a time limit for the race, allowing at least 30 minutes. After the race is over everyone must swap their recording sheets and check each other's work, using calculators if required. The winners are the ones who have finished their race in the fastest time *and* have done all their calculations correctly.

## Differentiation

**Less confident learners** might work only on the route, specifying distances travelled between locations and the overall distance travelled. They should do the standard race (see *Scenario guidelines*).

**More confident learners** should try the *Harder challenges*, calculating journey times and considering fuel requirements.

## Review

Once the winners have been established discuss difficulties, tactics and useful points. How could the children improve on their times for the next race?

## Further ideas

- With appropriate information and resources to hand, this activity can be repeated in many ways, such as stopping at the four capital cities, or six famous tourist attractions, in as fast a time possible.
- More confident children might use online tools to see how long the races would take if done by car.

# Scenario guidelines — Chase UK

## The 'Chase UK' challenge

In this game you get to fly a helicopter around the UK! The challenge is to start in a particular place, fly to John O'Groats and Land's End, then back to your starting point in as fast a time as possible. But you must not run out of fuel. There are lots of helicopter fuelling stations around the UK for you to use.

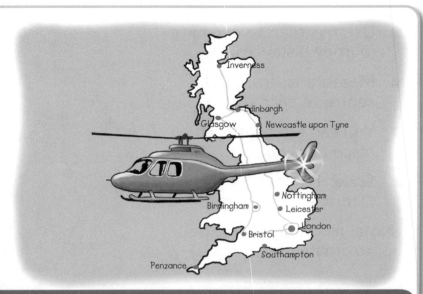

## Rules

- The race starts at midday (12.00 hours or 12 noon).
- You cannot fly to a place if you do not have enough fuel to get there.
- Stopping at any place requires a 10-minute break to change pilots, eat and so on.
- A stop to refuel requires a 30-minute break.
- Helicopters can fly a maximum of 200 miles before refuelling.

## Tips for calculating times and fuel requirements

- At 60 miles per hour, it takes one minute to travel one mile.
- At 120 miles per hour, it takes one minute to travel two miles.
- Stopping times – always remember to add on 10 minutes for a normal stop or 30 minutes for a refuelling stop.

## Quick race

- Everyone must start at John O'Groats and finish at Land's End.
- All helicopters fly at 60 miles per hour.
- You must not run out of fuel.

## Standard race

- All helicopters fly at 60 miles per hour.
- You can start anywhere you like (you can even mark your own home town on the map and start there).
- You must visit Land's End and John O'Groats, in any order.
- You must finish where you started.
- You must not run out of fuel.

- Use this map to estimate journey distances.
- Measure to/from the centre of each dot.
- You can refuel at each place marked.
- Scale: 1cm = 25 miles (1mm = 2.5 miles).

(Note: all distances will be approximate at this scale.)

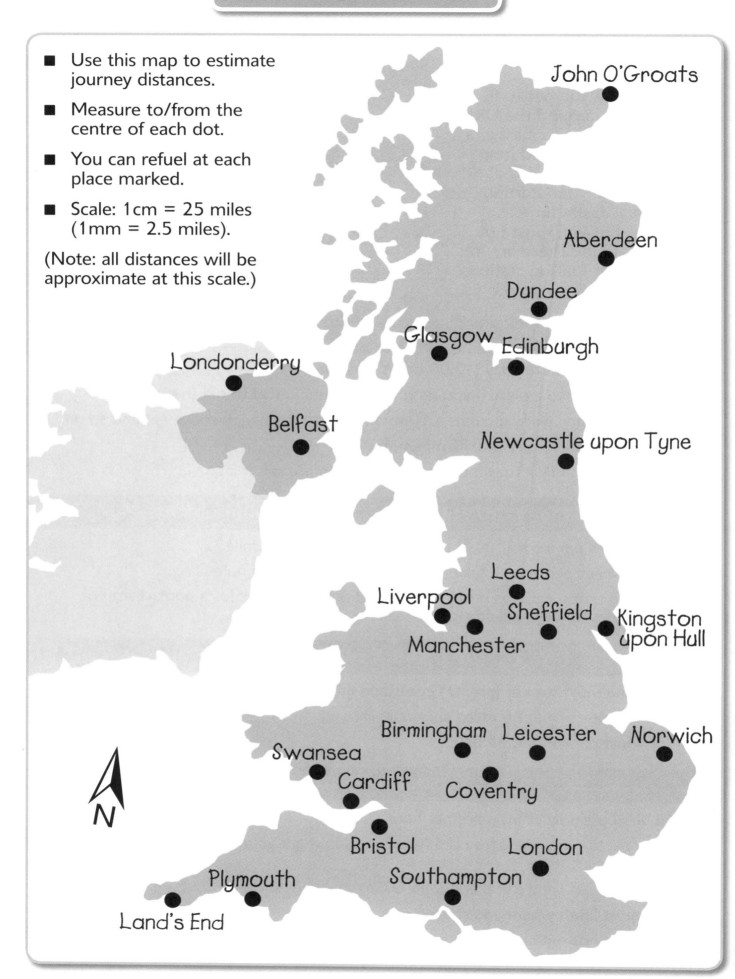

Name(s): _____

Starting point: _____

Race level: _____

Finishing point: _____

Your helicopter travels at a speed of: _____ mph.

- The race starts at 12 noon.
- You do not have to use every line of this chart.

| | From | To | | Miles travelled | Flight time | Arrival time | Refuel? | Time on the ground | Take-off time |
|---|---|---|---|---|---|---|---|---|---|
| First leg | | | | | | | | | |
| Second leg | | | | | | | | | |
| Third leg | | | | | | | | | |
| Fourth leg | | | | | | | | | |
| Fifth leg | | | | | | | | | |
| Sixth leg | | | | | | | | | |
| Seventh leg | | | | | | | | | |
| Eighth leg | | | | | | | | | |
| Ninth leg | | | | | | | | | |
| Tenth leg | | | | | | | | | |
| Eleventh leg | | | | | | | | | |
| Twelfth leg | | | | | | | | | |

Total miles travelled = _____

Time finished = _____

# Planet power

## Overview
Children must interpret a report containing a range of information and present it in a way that is meaningful and easy to understand.

## Timescales
- Lesson 1 (approximately 1 hour): Introduce the concepts; children read the report and begin to plan a presentation.
- Lesson 2 (at least 1 hour): Children prepare their presentations.
- Lesson 3 (approximately 1 hour): Children deliver and discuss their presentations.
- Extension: Develop skills further by creating draft presentations using the data in new ways, for example, by investigating the relationship between distance from the Sun and average temperature.

## Maths covered
Understanding and using very large numbers; rounding and estimating; data handling and interpretation.

## Prior learning
Experience of place value and rounding and estimating with larger numbers would be beneficial.

## Cross-curricular links
- Literacy: speaking and listening; reading.
- Science: Earth and the solar system.
- ICT: data handling.

## CD-ROM resources list
- Scenario video and slideshow.
- Data handling tools to produce graphs.
- Photocopiables: *Scenario guidelines*, *Planet facts*, *Solar system facts*, *Presentation plan*, *Solar system*, *Planets*, a *Factfile* for each planet, *Map of the Moon*, *Useful space links*.

## Resources list
Pencils, paper, books about the solar system if possible, calculators (optional), ICT suite with internet access (optional).

## Setting the scene
Watch the introductory film and show *Planet facts* and *Solar system facts*. Explain to the class that their task will be to interpret some of this information and create a presentation that is easy to understand. You will need to spend some time

at the beginning working through the *Scenario guidelines* with the whole class, ideally displaying them on an IWB. Ensure that all children understand rounding and simplifying numbers for ease of use, and that they appreciate the use of diagrams and charts to help visualise information. In particular, spend time looking at both data tables on *Planet facts*. The first table provides general information for each planet, whereas the second one is all about comparison with Earth. Model and discuss a range of simple conclusions that the data might reveal, such as: *Venus is roughly the same size as the Earth, but its days last more than a hundred times longer than Earth's do – it must spin very slowly on its axis.*

## Running the scenario
Arrange the children in pairs or small groups, as desired. Distribute or display the *Scenario guidelines*, and provide each pair or group with a copy of *Planet facts*, *Solar system facts* and *Presentation plan*. In lesson 1, stress that the children should focus on *planning* their presentations. It is essential that they have plenty of time to consider the data available and what it might usefully show. Presentations can be done on paper or on a computer depending on the needs of the class.

## Differentiation
**Less confident learners** should be helped to round numbers to make them more manageable. They might also avoid creating charts and simply focus on comparing planets through estimation, diagrams and interesting facts.
**More confident learners** should consider using written methods to calculate comparisons more accurately, and produce appropriate graphs or charts.

## Review
When reviewing the presentations consider whether the children can represent data appropriately. In particular, check that they can round numbers and estimate accurately, and look for meaningful deductions and ideas about what the data suggests.

## Further ideas
Conduct further research into a planet. Study the Sun – the largest, hottest body of the solar system – or the Moon. See *Useful space links* for some interesting websites, the *Factfile* for each planet, *Solar system*, *Planets* and the *Map of the Moon*.

### Understanding the solar system

Many people know good rhymes to help them remember the order of the planets, but the solar system is much more interesting than that! For hundreds of years, astronomers and scientists have been discovering more and more about it, passing down knowledge over the centuries and using increasingly advanced technology. We now have lots of detailed information about the Sun and all the planets. We can use this to understand more about the system we live in.

### Using very large numbers

Sometimes numbers get so big that we need easier ways to understand them. For example, the diameter (that's the distance across the middle) of Earth is **12,756km.** Now, if you know place value you will see that this is twelve thousand, seven hundred and fifty-six kilometres.

But look at this number: the average distance of Earth from the Sun is approximately **150,000,000km**, or one hundred and fifty million kilometres. We can make this easier to read by writing **150 million kilometres**.

### Making good use of information

The important thing is not just showing the information, it is what you learn from it. It is up to you what facts you try to deduce. As you read the report think about what you want to try and learn from the data.

- We can use the information we have to compare facts about the planets, as long as we use the same units.
  - For example, on average Saturn is 1,426,000,000km from the Sun. We can make this easier by saying that Saturn is 1,426 million kilometres from the Sun.
  - So, Earth is 150 million kilometres from the Sun and Saturn is 1,429 million kilometres from the Sun.
  - We can use these numbers to deduce that Saturn is nearly 10 times further away from the Sun than Earth is.

### Making charts and presenting information with large numbers

You may find that making charts or diagrams about the solar system is difficult. How can you draw a chart to fit in very large numbers? Or, when some numbers are much bigger than others on your chart (such as the diameters of the planets) the smaller numbers can become tiny dots. If you do have these problems, the second table of information on *Planet facts* might be useful. This compares all the planets to Earth.

## Planet data

This information has been simplified, but can still help us to understand the size and scale of the solar system.

| Planet | Average distance from the Sun (millions of km) | Diameter (km) | Day length (Earth hours) | Orbit time (Earth days) | Average temp. (°C) | No. of Moons | Rings? |
|---|---|---|---|---|---|---|---|
| Mercury | 58 | 4878 | 4223 | 88 | 167 | 0 | no |
| Venus | 108 | 12,104 | 2808 | 225 | 480 | 0 | no |
| Earth | 150 | 12,756 | 24 | 365 | 20 | 1 | no |
| Mars | 228 | 6794 | 24.5 | 687 | −65 | 2 | no |
| Jupiter | 778 | 142,800 | 10 | 4329 | −110 | 63 | yes |
| Saturn | 1426 | 120,000 | 10.5 | 10,735 | −180 | 62 | yes |
| Uranus | 2871 | 51,120 | 17 | 30,675 | −216 | 27 | yes |
| Neptune | 4497 | 49,528 | 16 | 60,152 | −216 | 13 | yes |

## Comparing other planets to Earth

This information has also been simplified, but still helps us to compare the other planets with Earth. Here each result for Earth is given as 1 and the results for the other planets are given in relation to this.

| Planet | Distance from the Sun | Diameter | Rotation time (Earth days) | Orbit time (Earth years) | Mass | Gravity |
|---|---|---|---|---|---|---|
| Mercury | 0.4 | 0.4 | 59 | 0.25 | 0.05 | 0.4 |
| Venus | 0.7 | 0.95 | 243 | 0.6 | 0.8 | 0.9 |
| Earth | 1 | 1 | 1 | 1 | 1 | 1 |
| Mars | 1.5 | 0.5 | 1 | 2 | 0.1 | 0.4 |
| Jupiter | 5 | 11 | 0.4 | 12 | 318 | 2.5 |
| Saturn | 9.5 | 9.5 | 0.4 | 29 | 95 | 1.1 |
| Uranus | 19 | 4 | 0.7 | 84 | 15 | 0.9 |
| Neptune | 30 | 4 | 0.7 | 165 | 17 | 1.1 |

The following source has been used but some of the data is approximate:
**http://hyperphysics.phy-astr.gsu.edu/hbase/solar/soldata2.html#c1**

**Your task:** Create an interesting presentation using some of the information about our solar system provided on the *Planet facts* and *Solar system facts* sheets. You should use this sheet to plan your presentation. Before you start, read the guidelines below.

## About the data

- The data in the charts has been simplified a little.
- Remember to look at the units involved, whether they are Earth days, kilometres or millions of kilometres, for example.
- In the *Planet facts* report, the first chart has much bigger numbers in it, but it is easier to use. The second chart compares the other planets with Earth (for example, Uranus is 9.5 times further from the Sun than Earth).
- It is fine to estimate and round off numbers.

## Tips for a strong presentation

- Be sure to spend some time looking at the information and making sure everyone in your group agrees on what you want your presentation to be about. You may want to focus just on one planet, or maybe compare two planets in different ways. Or you may want to compare the whole solar system based on important features, such as distances from the Sun.
- Decide carefully whether to use paper or ICT.
- Try to finish your presentation with some interesting thoughts or questions.

## Our focus

Write here what you want your report to be about.

## Information we will need

Note here the data you will need.

## Our presentation

Write here how you intend to lay out your presentation, including the charts you will prepare, and how you might deliver it to the rest of the class.

# Table-top qwick cricket

## Overview

Children work in pairs or small groups to compete in a dice-based qwick cricket league.

## Timescales

- Lesson 1 (approximately 1 hour): Introduce the concept, demonstrate game play and play a sample game.
- Lesson 2 (at least 1 hour): Run the league, collate the results and find the champions.
- Further lessons (at least 1 hour): Vary the rules as desired (see *Blank cricket ground* for a blank plan) to sustain interest, or introduce the harder version of the game which covers the times tables up to 12.
- Extension: If the children have been asked to track their individual players' performances (runs scored, wickets taken) during all their games there is now an opportunity for more confident children to make some interesting deductions. What was the highest score? The lowest? The average? Who should get the 'Player of the year' award? If desired, introduce two dice for bowling; how might this affect the rules?

## Maths covered

2-, 3-, 4- and 5-times tables (the standard game goes up to 5 × 5; the harder game goes up to 12 × 5); adding one- and two-digit numbers up to and over 100.

## Prior learning

Children should be familiar with their 2-, 3-, 4- and 5-times tables, and adding two-digit numbers up to and beyond 100.

## Cross-curricular links

- Literacy: speaking and listening.
- PE: awareness of different sports.

## CD-ROM resources list

- Scenario video and slideshow.
- League table chart.
- Photocopiables: *Scenario guidelines, Match scorecards, Plan of cricket ground, Blank cricket ground, Kwik cricket rules* and *Blank league table template.*

## Resources list

Pencils, paper, dice (one or two per team).

## Setting the scene

Show the children the introductory animation on the CD-ROM and read through the rules (see *Scenario guidelines*). It is important that the children understand the key cricketing terms, and rules for this game. Study the *Scenario guidelines* with the class and explain which version of the game they should play. Using the plan on the CD-ROM and some dice, ensure that everyone has a clear understanding of how to play the game through a demonstration: play a game together, asking for answers to calculations as appropriate.

## Running the scenario

For the league, arrange the children in pairs or small groups (there needn't be one cricketer per child). The ideal league should have eight teams in it, so you may opt for larger teams or two simultaneous leagues, perhaps differentiated. Distribute or display *Scenario guidelines, Match scorecards* and *Plan of cricket ground;* distribute dice appropriately. Give the children time to name their teams, agree on how they will allocate roles between themselves (such as representing two players each, responsibility for monitoring scores and so on), and colour in and cut out their counters from *Match scorecards.* Plan a system of rotation in advance so that every team plays every other team once. Ask the children to track each of their players' performance if they are going to examine the results (see Extension). For children who are finding the game too complicated, ignore the rule about stopping runs. Complete the *Blank league table template* as a class on an IWB at the end of the activity.

## Differentiation

**Less confident learners** should focus on the times tables aspect. **More confident learners** could be encouraged to track all the player scores (see Extension), do all calculations mentally and/or play the harder version.

## Review

Once a final league table has been created discuss whether the children think the rules are fair. Would they change them? How might they improve the game? (Use *Blank cricket ground* as a template for a new game.)

## Further ideas

- Bowl with two dice to cover higher times tables.
- Using a ready-made set of number cards, adapt the rules to focus on, say, factors or prime numbers. For example, if 64 is turned over, score 32 runs for naming the highest factor, four runs for naming 4 as a factor, and so on.
- Organise a real kwik cricket game (see *Kwik cricket rules*).

## Rules for matches

- There are four cricketers per team.
- Roll the dice to see who starts. The highest rollers bat first: this is 'Team A'.
- Team B position their players on the 'cricket ground'. Players must leave their section empty when they go to bowl.
- Team A must put their first cricketer by the wicket. The rest must wait for their turn to bat.
- Each innings lasts for four overs (there are six balls/rolls of the dice by the bowler per over) unless the batting team are all out before that.
- Each player in Team B bowls six balls (one over) then returns to their section, then the next player has a turn.
- After each roll of the dice by the bowler, the batsperson rolls the dice too (see below).
- If a batsperson is out they must change places with a new batter.
- At the end of the innings add up all your runs. (The other team must check your calculations.)
- After both teams have batted and added their runs the highest-scoring team wins the match. If both have the same total the match is a draw.

## Bowling and fielding

*Remember, the bowler rolls then the batsperson rolls.*

**Bowler rolls a 1** – *lbw (leg before wicket) appeal* – if the batsperson rolls a 1 or 6 they are out, if not there are no runs scored.

**Bowler rolls a 6** – *clean bowled!* – the batsperson is out. There are no runs scored.

**Bowler rolls a 2, 3, 4 or 5** – the batsperson can hit the ball into that section of the ground and runs can be scored! Now the batsperson must roll...

**Fielding** – the bowling team also roll to field the ball. If the bowling team have a fielder in the section of the ground (section 2, 3, 4 or 5) that the batsperson has hit the ball to, that fielder has a chance of stopping all the runs. If they can roll the same number as the batsperson they have stopped the ball, and no runs are scored. Any other number means the batsperson scores the runs.

## Standard version

- When batting, roll one dice only. This limits times tables practice to the five-times table, but is good for faster games.

## Harder version

- When batting, roll two dice for full times tables practice. Use two different coloured dice and decide in advance which one will be used for being caught, LBW appeals and fielding actions.

## Rules for the league

- Every team must play every other team once:
  - Win = 3 points
  - Draw = 1 point each
  - Loss = 0 points
- At the end of a game both teams must note the score and then calculate the run difference and points scored. Then they can play the next team.
- After all games, the team with the most points wins the league.
- Use most runs scored to decide a tie.

## Batting

*Remember, the bowler rolls then the batsperson rolls.*

**Batsperson rolls a 6** – they have been caught and they are out. There are no runs scored.

**Batsperson rolls a 1, 2, 3, 4 or 5** – the batsperson scores whatever they rolled multiplied by whatever the bowler has just rolled (2, 3, 4 or 5). For example, $4 \times 5 = 20$ runs.

*Remember that the fielder might have to roll now.*

# Match scorecards — Table-top qwick cricket

**Your name(s)**_____  **Team name**_____

- For each game, record your players' scores on rough paper, something like this:

| **Batting** (runs scored) | **Bowling** (wickets taken) |
|---|---|
| Batter A – 6, 4, 15, 16, OUT – total runs = 41 | Bowler A – // |
| Batter B – OUT – total runs = 0 | Bowler B – 0 |
| Batter C – 5, 12, 15, 2, 25, 8, OUT – total runs = 67 | Bowler C – / |
| Batter D – 2, 9, 6, 3, 20, OUT – total runs = 40 | Bowler D – / |
| **Total for the innings = 41 + 0 + 67 + 40 = 148** | |

- Record all your team's results below. You do not have to complete every row if there are not enough teams to play against.

| Your opponents | Runs scored by your team | Runs scored against your team | Win, draw or loss? | Points (Win = 3 Draw = 1 Loss = 0) |
|---|---|---|---|---|
| 1 | | | | |
| 2 | | | | |
| 3 | | | | |
| 4 | | | | |
| 5 | | | | |
| 6 | | | | |
| 7 | | | | |
| **Total** | | | | |

- Use this chart to track each player's performance through the league.

| Player | Runs scored | Wickets taken | Star rating |
|---|---|---|---|
| A | | | |
| B | | | |
| C | | | |
| D | | | |

- Colour in and cut out your players' counters to use in the games.

■ This represents the cricket pitch that you will play your games on.

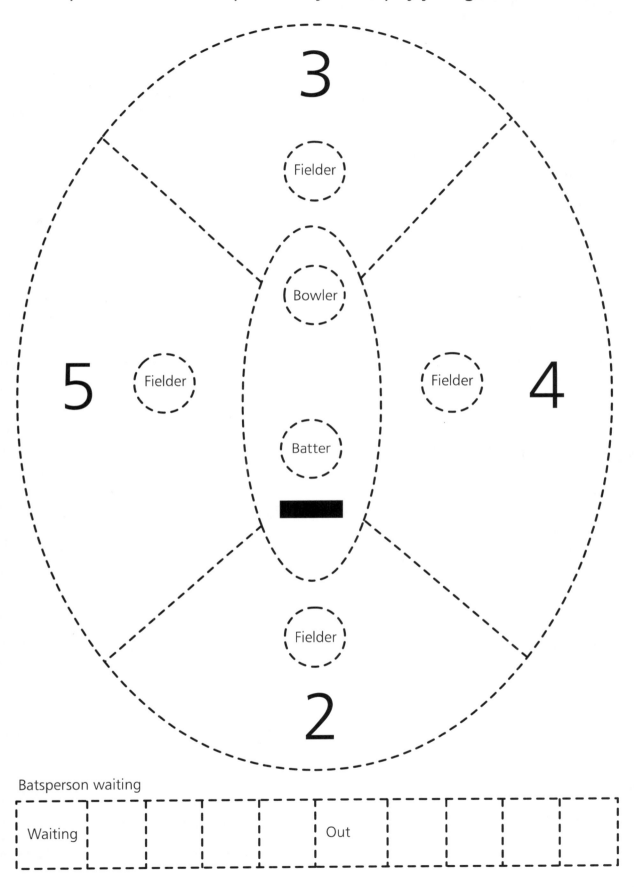

Batsperson waiting

| Waiting | | | | Out | | | | |
|---------|---|---|---|-----|---|---|---|---|

# Tips and ideas

While it might be too time consuming for teachers to develop resources like those in this book, there are many opportunities to incorporate meaningful maths into engaging lessons. First and foremost, remember that 'word problems' are fine, but they are not the same as scenario-based activities where the maths is an integral part rather than an end in itself. As such, the following checklist and ideas have been provided as a starting point for developing your own activities:

**Consider the context** – make sure the activities use maths in a meaningful way.

**Consider cross-curricular links** – think about how maths is involved in each area of the curriculum.

**Money money money** – given that most maths we do in adult life centres around money, there should be no problem developing new ideas around cash.

**Differentiation** – this is the trickiest part of developing your own resources. Do you want to really challenge children, or consolidate their existing skills? (A mixture of both is recommended over time.)

**Presenting work** – how children present their work is very important for successful real-life maths work. Consider whether you want children to follow tight guidelines or allow them more freedom. The latter is particularly liberating for those used to laying out work in prescriptive ways.

**Discussing work** – we allow children to look at and discuss each other's literacy and topic work, so why not their maths? Talking about how they have presented their work, as well as the actual maths, can consolidate understanding.

# Starting points

## Your school

- What's the budget for your classroom? How much do you spend on paper, books, pencils and so on? Could you make any savings and use the money for other things?
- Survey child and teacher travel habits. Estimate how much fuel is used getting everyone to and from school each day.
- Use brochures to design and cost a new garden or play area for the school.
- Monitor your time for a real school day, and compare this to the suggested timetable. How much time is spent working and playing? Is any time lost?
- Why are school meals the price they are? What is the daily budget of a school kitchen?

## Children's lives

- Create a pictogram of all the pets in the class. Ask pupils with pets to track their eating habits, the cost of food and other expenses. They could work in groups to calculate how much it costs to keep a pet – per week, per month, per year.
- Ask children to keep track of their time for a week. Compare habits and attitudes to accepted norms.
- If children receive pocket money ask them to track their income and spending for a week. Who spends wisely, and who is extravagant? Be sensitive to the fact that pocket money and household incomes may vary considerably.

## Charity and enterprise

- Support children in running stalls and events to raise funds for charities.
- Run your own Scholastic Book Fair: **www.bookfairs.scholastic.co.uk/business_school**